SEASHORE

Galley Press

CONTENTS

Author
David Lambert

Editor
John Paton

Illustrators
Graham Allen
Phil Weare
Brian Pearce

Copyright © 1977, 1983 by Grisewood & Dempsey Ltd.

Published in this edition by Galley Press, an imprint of W. H. Smith and Son Limited, Registered No. 237811 England.

Trading as WHS Distributors, St John's House, East Street, Leicester, LE1 6NE.

ISBN 0 86136 911 4

Printed and bound by Vallardi Industrie Grafiche, Milan, Italy

SEASHORE

The seashore is the ribbon of land that rims a country where it meets a sea or ocean. A shore's seaward edge is the lowest level bared by tides or winds. Its landward limit is the highest level splashed by spray. Various types of rocks, winds, and waves come together to forge different kinds of shore. These may be rocky, sandy, muddy, or made of coral. Some are backed by cliffs or sand dunes. Many of these places are homes for fascinating plants and animals.

Among the smallest creatures are the hatchling seashore animals in the water at the sea's edge. They belong to the plankton – the little drifting life forms that turn the sea's surface into a nourishing soup for the seashore animals that feed upon it and themselves make food for larger animals. Plant-like creatures, worms, insects, crabs, shellfish, starfish, fishes, turtles, birds, and seals – all grow, feed, or breed at or very near the sea's edge. Yet while most can withstand wave-buffeting, their lives are fragile. Spilt oil or chemicals can turn a living beach into a graveyard. Unless man treats the shore with care he risks destroying one of nature's most enchanted places.

Wind-driven waves batter a rocky coast. Where the sea's attack succeeds it carves sea cliffs in the land's rim.

Three stages in the formation of a sea cliff. Above: the land slopes steadily down to and below the sea.

As waves begin attacking the sloping coast, they start to cut a notch into the land. The broken rocks pile up on the sea bed.

Later still, the notch bites deeply and the undercut slope will collapse to leave a cliff. This faces an underwater, wave-cut platform.

Cliffs

Sometimes there is a rapid rise in sea level or a fall in the level of the land. Either way, waves may undercut the coast and carve out cliffs. Hardy plants and seabirds may colonize these steep and salty slopes.

Many a traveller's first glimpse of England is the White Cliffs of Dover. These world-famous walls of chalk tower sheer above the English Channel. Yet thousands of years ago there were no cliffs where they stand, and land joined England to France. Since then, the sea has moved in, cutting off England from mainland Europe. Near Dover the sea still gnaws into England's rim. From time to time masses of rock crash down into the shallow waters. There the sea sets to work to break up the rock and wash it away. Wherever sea attacks high land so fiercely it carves out cliffs.

In this war with the land the sea's weapons are water, air, stones and water's power to dissolve. Currents set off by the tides and waves whipped up by gales batter many a coastline. As waves smack against the foot of a cliff they cram air into rock crannies. When the waves retreat the air expands with explosive force, widening the cracks in the rock. Any bits of stone that break off join the sea's artillery of boulders, pebbles and sand grains with which waves bombard and weaken the cliff face. The sea's attack goes on even in calm weather, for water dissolves some rocks.

Different kinds of Cliff

Different kinds of rock help to give rise to various types of sea cliff. Hard rocks such as granite, limestone and Old Red sandstone tend to wear away slowly and produce steep cliffs. But sands, clays and gravels break down quickly. Blocks of such loose material may slide from a cliff top to leave a steep upper slope above gently shelving rubble which the sea soon plucks away.

The steepness of a cliff also varies with the angle at which rock layers lie. Layers tilted down toward the sea break off so as to leave a steep cliff. Backward tilted layers give a gentler slope.

Vertical cracks produce their own special cliff features. Water that enters and broadens a vertical crack may carve out a cave. Sometimes the sea bores a cave right through a headland. If the cave roof collapses, the tip of the headland may be cut off as a stack – a pinnacle of rock standing out as an offshore island. On some coasts, resistant and easily worn away rocks both reach the sea close together. The resistant rocks stand out as headlands. The rest are cut back and leave bays.

Thrift's tight, wind-resistant cushions of narrow leaves, with small, rounded heads of pink flowers, grow on many cliffs. These ground-hugging plants are designed to survive fierce gales.

Left: Sea cliffs cut in soft rocks have a fairly gentle slope.

Guillemots are safe on the rocky ledges of cliffs too steep for landbound predators to scale. Here these seabirds lay their eggs. If dislodged, each pear-shaped egg tends to rotate around its narrow end instead of simply rolling off a ledge into the sea.

Life on Sea Cliffs

Plants and animals of sea cliffs must somehow cope with steep slopes, salty spray and strong winds. Few living things can make their homes on sheer cliffs or cliffs that are always crumbling. But firm cliffs with gentle slopes or many cracks and ledges may bear a carpet of grasses and bright flowers.

Finding a roothold can be difficult. The tiniest rock crevice will trap a little soil where seeds may lodge and grow, but winds that dry the soil kill many cliffside seedlings. Others are torn up by gales. The survivors tend to be long-lived kinds of plant with tough, woody roots as anchors, and stems that give when the wind blows or always grow lopsidedly. Only salt-tolerant plants can stand the lowest levels of a sea cliff, where salty spray drenches air and soil alike. Inland types of plant grow higher up.

Birds are among the few animals that find sea-cliff footholds. On lonely coasts seabirds such as guillemots and gannets may nest on rocky ledges in their millions, safe from such landbound predators as rats and foxes.

Rocky Shores

Storms, baking, chilling, and drying up threaten the life forms that cling to the rocks.

A rocky shore is a battleground where the sea is attacking the land. Everywhere you see signs of the struggle: rock bared by the waves; boulders torn from the land, tossed onto the shore, and smoothed by the sea; hollows scoured in the bedrock and holding pools when the tide falls or an offshore wind blows.

Life on this battleground is often risky. Huge storm waves sometimes hammer the rocks. Tidal shores suffer daily drying and dousing as the sea level sinks and rises. At low tide in summer exposed rocks heat up sharply by day, but cool quickly at night. Also, rainwater flowing onto the shore sometimes dilutes the salt water at the sea's edge.

Only plants and animals that can stand up to these fast changing conditions could live between high and low tide levels. Many creatures of rocky shores have developed ingenious techniques for endurance.

Battering is no disaster for those organisms that live fixed to rocks. The soft, flexible bodies and stems of hydroids and seaweeds simply bend with the waves. Barnacles and limpets grow hard outer cases that guard their tender insides. And, agile creatures like crabs and shrimps

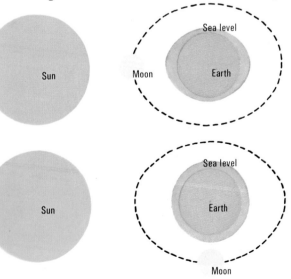

The daily rise and fall of the sea is due to the pull of gravity exerted on the oceans by the sun and moon. When the pulls of sun and moon combine (above left) a great double bulge of water travels through the oceans around the earth, causing the extra high and low tides called spring tides. When sun and moon pull in different directions, below left, the difference in level between high and low tides is slight. Such tides are called neap tides.

can creep under rocks to escape the full force of a storm.

Crabs, shore fishes, and sea worms all avoid drying out by seeking shelter and shade under seaweeds and boulders in rock pools. To preserve body moisture, barnacles shut their shells, and limpets press themselves against rocks. Certain sea anemones produce a sticky substance that helps keep them damp. Some seaweeds can lose most of their moisture without dying.

Most sea creatures can get all the oxygen they need from the air dissolved in water. But creatures living high (and thus often dry) on rocky shores make some use of atmospheric air. For instance, bar-

Finding Food Among the Rocks

The rocky shore may be a battleground, but it is also a sanctuary – a provider of homes and food for millions of organisms. We have already seen something of the variety of ways in which plants and animals find shelter. Dwellers on rocky shores also get their food in many ways.

Barnacles, some shellfish and some sea worms are filter feeders, sieving tiny food particles from the water flowing past. On most shores, tides, currents or wind-borne waves wash in daily supplies of such food in the form of plankton – the minute drifting plants and animals that abound in ocean surface waters.

Certain shellfish and worms and the crabs eat detritus – edible titbits that settle on the sea floor. Limpets, topshells and sea urchins are grazers, nibbling the plants that grow on rocks. In so doing they slowly gnaw away the rocks themselves. Last of all come the beasts that prey on other animals. These predators include dog whelks, fishes, gulls, and man.

Patterns of Life

Plants and animals designed for different kinds of rocky seashore life do best at different levels on the shore. Tiny land plants called lichens – each part alga, part fungus – encrust rocks splashed only by the highest spray. But the largest seaweeds thrive only low down on the shore. Drought-resistant barnacles and winkles live happily at high-tide level, where most fishes and sponges would soon dry out and die.

Wherever they live, shore dwellers form part of a food pyramid – its broad base made up of plants, its tip of predators. Predators may use half the food they eat, but the herbivores (plant-eaters) lose nine-tenths of their food as body wastes. Thus a huge weight in plants goes to support a much smaller weight in herbivores, and this in turn props up a still smaller load of predators.

Looked at in another way, dwellers on the rocky shore make up a food web – an imaginary network of threads linking each kind of plant or animal with those it eats and (or) those that eat it.

You can design food pyramids and food webs for all the world's rocky shores except those scoured by ice. These alone are too harsh to support life.

nacles and limpets trap air in their shells, and tropical hermit and ghost crabs have evolved a kind of lung in addition to their gills that filter oxygen from water.

Thick cell walls and thick shells help to protect the tender parts of fixed plants and hard-topped animals from hot sun. And to avoid overheating, some tropical creatures let a little water evaporate from their bodies or from inside their shells. Winter weather is kinder on open shores than the weather inland, but cold spells can kill delicate shore dwellers and many escape to deep, warmer waters.

Green seaweeds are among those seashore inhabitants adapted to tolerate fresh water that seeps off the land.

Some plants and animals on a rocky shore. Plankton (1), sponge (2), anemone (3), sea urchin (4), horse mussel (5), acorn barnacle (6), shore crab (7), kelp (8), goby (9), common prawn (10), green seaweed (11), lichens (12), knotted wrack (13), bladder wrack)14), small periwinkle (15), limpet (16), dog whelk (17), turnstone (18). Some creatures move up on the shore as the tide rises and down as it drops.

Below: a section through a sandy shore shows some of the creatures buried there at low tide. From left to right: sand mason's tube (1), greater sand eel (2), mud crab (3), grass shrimp (4), heart urchin (5), cockle (6), lugworm (7), tellin (8), razor shell (9). Right: as the tide flows in, sand dwellers peep out. The sand mason (1) releases gills and tentacles: the heart urchin (5), tube feet; the shellfish, feeding tubes. Mason crabs (3) emerge only at night, and lugworms, never.

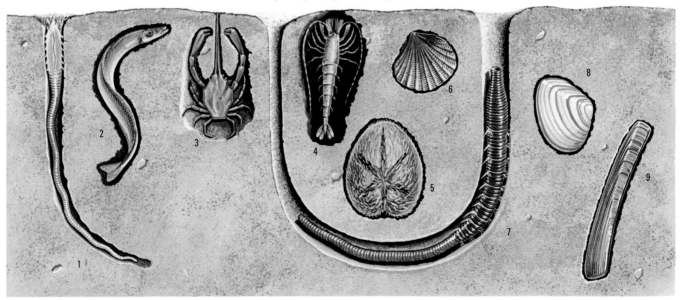

Sandy Shores

Rock fragments break into sand grains that build beaches. Plants cannot grow on the shifting sands, but countless creatures live beneath the surface.

A sandy beach backed by a palm-lined coast. Sand grains from which shores are built are tiny fragments worn away from cliffs or rocky coasts.

Next time you visit a sandy shore, run the sand through your fingers. Glasslike, transparent grains may be made of quartz, a form of silica also found as an important ingredient in granite and sandstone rocks. Other glassy grains may consist of flint, a form of silica that occurs as lumps in chalk. Very possibly, the sand grains in your hand were once part of granite, sandstone, or chalk cliffs. Under the sea's attack, the cliff fronts toppled and waves and wave-borne stones smashed the fallen rocks to bits. These then rubbed against each other until their edges were smoothed off. Thus the broken rocks became pebbles and many of these pebbles were worn down into sand grains.

Meanwhile, tides, waves and currents carried sands and pebbles away along the coast until waves dumped them on some gently shelving shore. So were born most sand and pebble beaches. (There are also beaches built of ground-up bits of shell and coral.)

Some beaches form where seaborne sands or pebbles catch on the tip of a peninsula and build a spit – a straight or curved beach, one end joined to land, the other flanked by sea. Then there are bars – long, narrow beach islands lying just offshore. Beaches also come in many sizes. Between rocky headlands they may be short and narrow. But vast, broad beaches fringe many a big bay on a low-lying coast. Almost wherever they grow, beaches begin to fill in dents in a crooked coast, and tend to make the coastline straighter. In this way, beaches build land at the sea's expense.

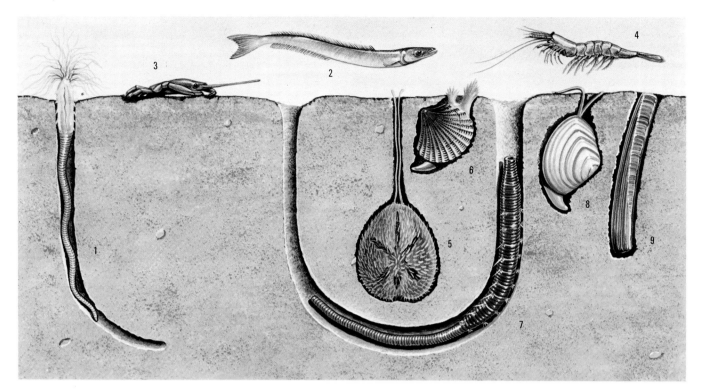

Life on a Sandy Shore

Your first glimpse of a sandy shore at low tide suggests a dismal desert. Only dead and dying seaweeds and shellfish litter the smooth surface. This is not surprising, for loose sand offers no foundation for the limpets, barnacles and seaweeds that cling to the firm surfaces of rocky shores. On the other hand, many creatures can and do live or move beneath the sands.

Look carefully at the lower beach and you will see tiny pits and bumps that betray some of these teeming cave dwellers. Their shyness provides these little miners with real benefits. They can lie up untroubled by pounding waves and hidden from the eyes of predators that stalk the surface. They also keep comfortably moist because spaces between sand grains hold water, even when the tide has fallen. And because beach sands a mere handsbreadth deep never grow very hot or cold, sun or frost can bake or chill the beach above without bothering the burrowers. Most important of all, creatures living in the sands have daily food supplies delivered to their very doors by tides and waves.

Tiny white worms, seaweed fly maggots, beetles, and sandhoppers gorge on the heaps of decaying weed tossed up along the strandline. In the middle level of the beach live other animals. Some sea worms live entirely underground, feeding on food sifted from the sand. When the tide sweeps in, shellfish, crabs, certain sea worms, and other animals eat food scraps lying on the sandy surface. Then, too, there are shellfish and other creatures that suck plankton from the water above. Low down on the beach, where only the lowest tides lay bare the sands, live flatfishes, sand eels, crabs, and starfish.

Many hunters prowl the sands. Gulls and wading birds with beaks like tweezers patrol the shore to probe for insects, sandhoppers, worms and shellfish. In the shallow waters, hungry fishes watch for signs of life. Man, too, comes seeking worms for bait, and shrimps for food. In spite of their protective sandy covering, millions of seashore creatures end up in someone's stomach.

Here, sand drifting along a coast from left to right catches on a peninsula and forms a spit.
In the second diagram, sand moved along both sides of a peninsula piles up beyond to create a beach poking out to sea.
Here, rocky headlands halt the drift of sand. Sand collects in the coves and builds a beach curving around each little bay.

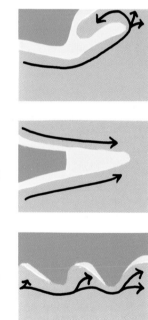

While sandy and rocky shores are rich in life forms, shingle beaches are largely barren. This reflects the size of their ingredients. Shingle beaches consist of pebbles – rounded rock fragments that may be as small as a little finger's fingernail or as large as a goose's egg. As waves crash on such a beach and then retreat they build a steep slope of stones that are often on the move. Pebbles rolling down the slope crush and kill plants or animals that chance to lodge there. What is more, the big gaps between the pebbles hold no moisture when the tide has fallen. In such conditions life is just impossible.

Sand Dunes

Sections through a sand dune show four stages in its growth.
1. Sands blown by the wind lodge against a young plant.
2. As leaves thrust through the sand, more lodges on them.
3. Underground stems release shoots that sprout above the growing dune.
4. Underground stems continue rising through the dune.
The plant may also throw out long underground stems from which new plants arise and build new dunes.

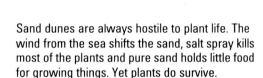

Sand dunes are always hostile to plant life. The wind from the sea shifts the sand, salt spray kills most of the plants and pure sand holds little food for growing things. Yet plants do survive.

Sands blown up the beach may lodge against patches of shoregrass and build up low, shifting sand hills. In time, plants cover the hills and bind their sands together.

How Dunes are Formed

Few places seem so hostile to living things as the upper shores of sandy beaches. Onshore winds send stinging sand grains hissing up the shallow slopes. The windblown surface is always on the move, making it hard for plants to keep a roothold. Then, too, any rain that falls swiftly sinks down through the sands so that these quickly dry out, depriving shallow-rooted plants of moisture. Anyway, most of the moisture that lands is wind-blown sea spray, rich enough in salt to kill most kinds of land plant. Lastly, pure sand is poor in plant foods. Yet, in spite of all these hazards, hardy plants root on the foreshore. Eventually, onshore winds may pile sands against them to build the sandy humps we know as dunes.

The first plants to get a grip upon the upper beach are ones that tolerate salt spray, get nourishment from decomposed seaweed, and throw out roots faster than the wind can blow away the sands they grow in. Prickly saltwort, with thick, fleshy leaves, and the scruffy, crouching oraches are among these plant pioneers. But gales may tear them out, leaving only seeds to sprout next year.

The true dune builders lie farther from the sea. These plants are long lived grasses. On many sandy coasts sea couch grass (sword grass) is the first type that you meet as you walk inland. Sword grass traps loose sand in a web of roots. Its knee-high stems halt

wind-blown surface sands, which pile up into a low dune. Also its flexible, springy, hairy, inrolled leaves bend without snapping in the wind, and keep down water loss.

Unlike sword grass, marram grass cannot stand salt spray, and it grows behind the advance-guard grasses. But throughout the world, no plant is more effective than marram grass at trapping sand and raising dunes. As sands lodge against and swamp its waist-high leaves, fresh shoots thrust upward through the growing dune. There is no known limit to the length to which these plants can grow. Thus dune and marram grass both tend to go on rising until there is a line of dunes as high as houses, or even higher. In western France and southern Spain stand dunes as tall as skyscrapers.

How Dunes Change

Parts of a belt of dunes often migrate inland. This especially happens where rabbit burrows or footpaths clear a patch of dune vegetation. The wind blows loose sand from the steep, seaward face up and over the dune crest to produce a so-called blow-out. The wind-blown sand then drifts inland as a dune shaped like a new moon with seaward-facing horns. As they travel, some such dunes may swallow trees and buildings. New dunes grow up to take their place and gaps called slacks develop between the new dunes and the old. Sometimes whole rows of dunes and slacks appear.

Where marram grass has halted dunes, other plants move in, carpeting the sand and, when they die, providing nourishment for their successors. Thus dunes are truly fixed in place and fertile soil is formed. Where this happens, marram grass peters out and is replaced by lichens, mosses, heath, and sand sedge or comparable plants. Meanwhile, moisture-loving plants – creeping willow for example – colonize moist slacks. Eventually, what had been an area of barren ground provides a rich variety of homes for countless insects, spiders, reptiles, birds, and mammals.

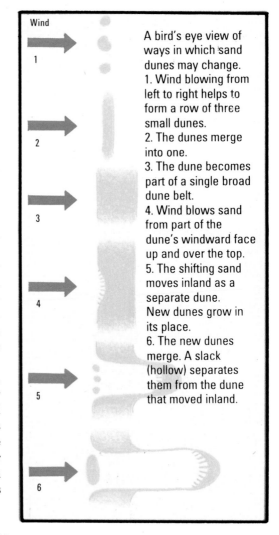

A bird's eye view of ways in which sand dunes may change.
1. Wind blowing from left to right helps to form a row of three small dunes.
2. The dunes merge into one.
3. The dune becomes part of a single broad dune belt.
4. Wind blows sand from part of the dune's windward face up and over the top.
5. The shifting sand moves inland as a separate dune. New dunes grow in its place.
6. The new dunes merge. A slack (hollow) separates them from the dune that moved inland.

Below: different types of dune support different kinds of plant. Here (left to right) saltwort grows on an upper shore. Sea couch grass and marram grass build moving dunes. Sand sedge colonizes fixed dunes. Heather creates dune heath. Creeping willow likes moist slacks. Turf grasses form dune meadow. Sea buckthorn is part of dune scrubs.

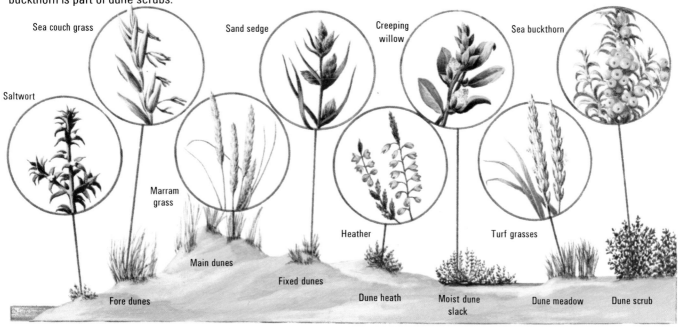

Sea couch grass — Sand sedge — Creeping willow — Sea buckthorn — Saltwort — Marram grass — Heather — Turf grasses — Main dunes — Fore dunes — Fixed dunes — Dune heath — Moist dune slack — Dune meadow — Dune scrub

Muddy Shores

Clay and silt washed to sea by rivers settle in calm waters and pile up as mud banks. Plants change mudbank into salt marsh and mangrove swamp.

Right: an Asian mangrove swamp hides a wealth of hunters and hunted. Top to bottom: The serpent eagle preys on crabs and birds. The crab-eating macaque and water snake eat crabs and mudskippers. The crab-eating frog catches crabs. The fiddler crab munches edible scraps. Catfish probe for food in mud. A mudskipper's diet may include snails. This marine snail eats edible debris.

In coastal waters sheltered from the winds and waves, bits of silt and clay smaller and lighter than sand grains can settle down and build up banks of mud. Such mudflats flank the mouth of many a sluggish river that has wound its way across a plain.

Just like a sandy shore, a muddy beach is home to countless tiny burrowers – creatures including sea worms, crabs, and shellfish. A square patch of mud one pace across may hold 10,000 worms or 20,000 tiny snails. Dwellers in estuary mud must be so made that the tiny close-packed particles in mud cannot block their breathing systems. They must also endure fresh water flowing downriver at low tide, and salty water surging upstream as the tide turns. Some are better than others at coping with changing saltiness. Shore crabs and common periwinkles can survive brackish water while flounders can flourish far upstream.

For estuary plants the biggest problem is the force with which the tides surge to and fro. Somehow, plants manage to take root here and there. Mud lodged against these pioneers builds low, tiny islands. In time, scores of islands separated by a web of ditches deeply scoured by tides rise above the estuary mud. Where this happens, mudflat has given birth to salt marsh.

In warm parts of the world, mangrove swamp, not salt marsh, thrives on muddy coasts. Mangrove seeds sprout while still on the tree and can quickly root in tidal waters. Waterlogged mud lacks oxygen, but mangrove roots can get this gas from air. Red mangroves throw down roots that grow like stilts from branches. Black mangroves produce roots bent up above the mud like knees. Another kind of mangrove has spear-like roots that thrust above the mud.

Dense mangrove forest provides homes for many creatures living in the mud and water, or among the leaves and branches of the trees. These animals include such curiosities as the crab-eating frog, the world's only frog able to live in salty water; and the mud-skipper, a tiny fish that walks and leaps about on land.

Gull's eye view of creeks meandering through a salt marsh. River water washed particles of mud down to the coast. There, the mud piled up around the roots of salt-tolerant plants. In time such plants raised low, soft islands, building land out into the sea.

Below: this slab cut from a salt marsh shows different plants that grow at different levels. From left to right we see eel grass, glasswort, and cord grass thriving between high and low tide levels. Sea purslane roots on the banks of a drainage channel. Sea rush and red fescue grass colonize the landward slope shown rising from a salt pan (an isolated tidal pool that dries up at low water).

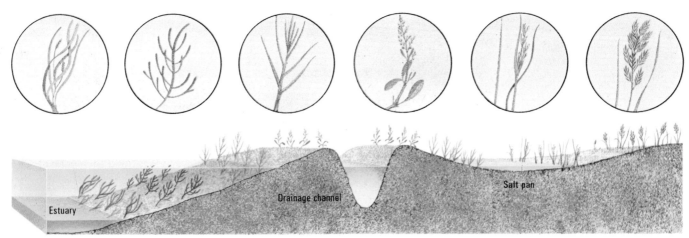

Estuary

Drainage channel

Salt pan

Coral Shores

Reef-building coral polyps

Cardinal, damsel, hawk and other coloured fishes feed and breed among living corals.

Some living things build coral reefs. Others destroy the reefs but help form coral beaches.

If you walk along a warm, tropical shore, the sands that crunch beneath your feet may consist of the crushed skeletons of billions of tiny coral-forming animals and plants.

Coral is a hard, limy, rocklike substance that grows under water. The coral-building animals or polyps resemble little sea anemones, but each lives in a protective limy cup. By day the polyps hide inside their cups. At night their tentacles poke out to catch the tiny living things

Reef-forming type of seaweed

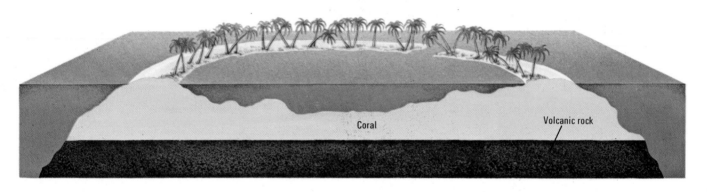

Coral

Volcanic rock

This slice cut through the middle of an atoll shows that its coral (pink) stands on a platform of volcanic rock (grey). As the sea drowned such islands, coral kept growing upward.

Parrot fish, a coral chewer that feeds on coral polyps

Palolo worm, a reef destroyer that burrows in dead coral

that form their food. When one generation of coral polyps dies its cups become the foundations upon which another generation of living polyps builds. Millions of polyps go to make one coral colony. Different growth patterns give rise to corals shaped in different ways: as fans, stags' horns, brains, and so on. But all such corals can grow only in warm, clear, shallow waters.

Besides the polyps, there are hard, limy, reef-building seaweeds. These can grow in surf too fierce for the coral polyps to survive.

Among crannies in the corals lurks a dazzlingly coloured array of damselfish, clownfish, surgeon fish, and other fishes especially designed to feed and hide here.

If the sea rises or their rock foundation sinks, coral-building plants and animals may build up reefs that keep pace with the changing water level. Reefs millions of years old may be more than 1,000 metres

thick. Yet their tops barely peep above the sea.

There are three kinds of coral reef. Fringing reefs are long, narrow coral platforms lying offshore beyond a shallow, narrow strip of water known as a lagoon. Barrier reefs are divided from the shore by a much broader channel. An atoll – the third kind of coral reef – is a narrow coral necklace encircling a lagoon.

The shores of coral islands such as atolls are largely built of dead, not living coral, which grows only under water. Coral may be killed or broken up in many ways. The crown of thorns starfish dissolves and digests living coral polyps. Palolo worms burrow in dead coral and help to break up reefs. Sea snails, date

mussels, and some clams dissolve and tunnel into coral limestone. Parrot fish crunch up coral cups to eat the juicy polyps. Such onslaughts break some coral into sand grains and so weaken coral outcrops that storm waves may snap them off and drive them up onto the reef. Lightweight coral sands blown and washed beyond this barrier can settle in the shelter of the lagoon to build a coral beach.

In time, hardy seashore plants and animals move in. Tough pemphis thorn, mangroves, and coconut palms are among the first arrivals – some taking root from seeds that may have drifted hundreds of kilometres on the ocean currents before the sea washed them up upon an atoll.

Best known creatures of coral shores are crabs which come in great variety and include burrowing, hermit, fiddler, robber, and soldier crabs. Many have air-breathing devices and need only an occasional dip in the sea to moisten their gills. These animals can venture well inland. Tropical hermit crabs, for instance, range about 200 metres from the sea to kill and eat seabird nestlings. Robber crabs – gigantic beasts measuring nearly a metre across – use their massive claws to hammer open coconuts so as to reach the pulp inside.

But atoll life is insecure. Fierce winds and waves can rake across these low islands, stripping plants and creatures from their shores.

A face mask shows the size of this robber crab. Immensely powerful, such a crab can escape from a tin crate or a wooden box with sides 2·5 cm thick. They live on islands in the Indian and Pacific oceans, where they feed on coconuts and dead animals. They possess special breathing organs, and need only a nightly dip in the sea. Robber crabs actually drown if kept entirely under water.

Seaweeds

Seaweeds need no true stems or roots. They draw support and nourishment from the surrounding water. Different species thrive at different depths.

Most of us see seaweeds as limp, slimy, rather ugly plants draped over rocks at low tide. Only when we glimpse them in a seashore pool do we marvel at the beauty of their fronds buoyed up by water. Then, too, we begin to realize that seaweeds grow in rich variety. They may be flimsy, rubbery, or hard; green, brown, red, pink, or purple. Some are so tiny that you would need a microscope to identify them. Others are long enough to be wrapped around a house.

Unlike those of flowering plants, seaweeds' bodies are not divided into true roots, stems, and leaves. In sea lettuce, the seaweed's body (called a thallus, by the way) lacks any special shape. Then, too, certain oarweeds have a simple, straplike frond. But in many seaweeds the different parts are variously designed and do in fact look much like true stems and leaves. There are red seaweeds with branchlets like the teeth of a comb, and others with feathery fronds. Coralline seaweeds have stiff, brittle 'stems'. The flat 'leaves' of bladderwrack have pea-sized air bladders that serve as floats to raise the seaweed as the tide moves in.

Seaweeds make the foods they need from chemicals that they absorb from the surrounding water. To do so these plants need the help of sunlight. But white sunlight is made of all the colours in the rainbow. Green seaweeds need the red in sunlight. This only penetrates the surface water. Thus green seaweeds cannot grow deep down. Red seaweeds, on the other hand, can use the blue in sunlight.

Sea lettuce (1) and *Enteromorpha* (2) are green seaweeds. Channeled (3), bladder (4) and toothed wrack (5) are brown. *Porphyra* (6) and *Pylaiella* (7) grow on the last two. The two red seaweeds are a *Dilsea* (8) and a Heterosiphonia (9). The big brown species are laminarians (10) and (11).

Japanese women clean and sort seaweed.

Blue light penetrates water more deeply than red, and red seaweeds grow 100 metres and more deep in clear, warm waters near the equator. All seaweeds belong to one of these three colour groups: green, red, or brown.

Because seaweeds get their nourishment from the surrounding water they need no roots to draw up nutrients and moisture. Instead of roots they rise from rootlike holdfasts which simply glue them onto rocks or shells or other seaweeds. Holdfasts take various forms including claws, sticky threads, and discs. Tethered to the sea bed by these anchors, some seaweeds can withstand the fiercest gales. Scientists have found that it takes a pull of 42 kilograms per square centimetre to snap a bladderwrack stalk. Even so, winter storms kill over half the wracks that grow off northern shores. Seaweeds may also be grazed upon and killed by limpets and topshells. Then, too, in Japan and elsewhere people eat these plants.

Those seaweeds surviving all disasters grow quickly and help to make good the loss of those destroyed. At least one brown seaweed can grow 30 metres in a year. Yet seaweeds come from tiny beginnings. Some start as plantlets growing on their parents' 'leaves'. Others sprout from runners thrown off by the parent plants. But many individuals spring from microscopic scraps of life called spores, produced in special spore-producing branches on the adult plants.

The Japanese are so fond of eating the red seaweed *Porphyra* that they have cultivated it for the last three centuries. In autumn, the seaweed farmers plant bamboo shoots in mud below water nearly two metres deep. Tiny *Porphyra* spores land on the shoots and start to grow. Next, the cultivators transplant the bamboo shoots near a river mouth. There, in diluted seawater, the seaweeds produce a crop of particularly large, tender plants. These are harvested, washed, chopped up, dried on trays, then bundled up and sold. Finally, housewives serve up the seaweed with balls of boiled rice. Some Welsh and Irish also eat *Porphyra* which they boil to make Laver bread — a jelly that is often fried with bacon.

Plant-like Animals

Most animals move about in search of food. But the sponges, sea anemones, sea mats, and sea squirts live fixed lives and wait for food to come to them.

Hunt carefully and you may find orange patches and tiny leafless 'twigs' growing on rocks low down on the shore. These plant-like objects are actually animals.

Sponges

Of all these plant-like creatures, sponges are built upon the simplest lines. Each lacks a head, mouth and separate body organs. But tiny holes in the sides let in water and with it food and oxygen. Cells equipped with whips thrash the water through the sponge's hollow body, which is stiffened by a skeleton of fibres or of little needles of silica and calcium carbonate – the chief ingredients in glass and limestone. Inside the sponge, cells absorb oxygen and scraps of food. The used water then squirts from the sponge's body through an outlet like a small

volcanic crater. With it go body wastes and sometimes baby sponges, which swim about before they settle down.

Many sponges grow in colonies resembling shrubs or vases, or simply forming shapeless blobs.

Hollow-Gutted Animals

Sea anemones, hydroids and jellyfish belong to the coelenterate or 'hollow-gutted' group of animals, so named because they have a pouch-shaped gut where they digest their food. One body entrance serves as mouth and drain for body waste. Most coelenterates have a circular body plan that reminds us of a daisy.

Indeed the sea anemone's very name suggests some gaily coloured flower. Many sea anemones are undoubtedly colourful.

Anemone feeding on a prawn. The prawn touched one of the anemone's tentacles. Stinging cells in the tentacles showered the prawn with tiny, paralyzing poison threads. The tentacles then pulled the victim down to the sea anemone's mouth.

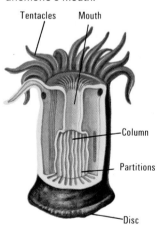

A sea anemone sliced down the middle to show its hollow body. Food passes from the tentacles through the mouth to the inside of the column where it is digested. Below is a disc that grips rocks.

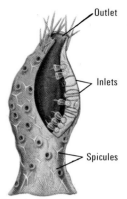

They may be blue, green, pink, or red. But the sea anemone's 'stalk' is a rubbery-jelly tube crowned not with petals but with tentacles that grab small fishes or other passing prey. Many sea anemones can also shoot out poison threads to sting and paralyze their victims. Finally, tentacles cram the victims' bodies in the sea anemone's mouth. If danger threatens, the creature pulls in its tentacles and shrinks into a squat lump.

Hydroids resemble groups of tiny sea anemones fixed to a hard stalk that may be as long as a finger. Each hydroid polyp thrusts out tentacles from the little cup in which it lives. These tentacles lash water into the minute creature's body, bringing with it oxygen and particles of food. In some species, certain polyps lack tentacles but grow saucer-shaped buds. One by one these develop into tiny jellyfish-like medusas that break free and swim away. The medusas lay eggs from which hatch larvae that eventually settle down and live fixed lives just like their grandparents. True jellyfish, too, produce fixed and free-swimming generations, but their free-swimming forms are much larger than those of hydroids.

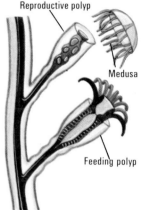

Above: a colony of hydroids. The diagram shows part of a colony with feeding and reproductive polyps. This feeding polyp (lower branch) has tentacles and stings. Tiny medusas float off from the reproductive polyp (upper branch).

Sea Mats

Sea mats are colonies of tiny animals forming lacelike patterns often shaped as seaweeds. Like hydroids, sea mats are armed with tentacles. 'Whips' sprouting from the tentacles lash lifegiving water in and out of the sea mats' bodies.

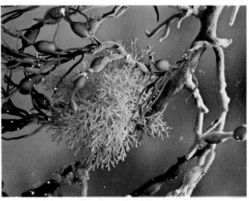

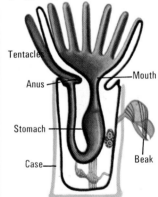

Above: moss animal colonies, and a section through a creature's body. Tiny whips lash food particles into the mouth. Food is digested in the stomach and waste leaves by the anus. The beak is a separate individual that catches small prey.

Sea Squirts

Sea squirts start as free-swimming 'tadpoles'. But in time most kinds stick headfirst to a rock or seaweed, lose their tails and become little blobs of red, brown, or green jelly. Tiny whips draw water into each sack-like creature through a special inlet. Waste water, body wastes, and eggs leave from a separate outlet. A scared sea squirt shrinks, forcing water from its body through these holes.

Right: sea squirts, plant-like animals growing on a rock. The diagram shows the mouth which draws in water and food by means of little whips around the gill slits. Waste leaves by a special outlet.

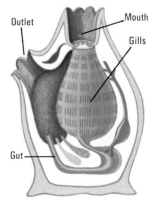

Sea Worms

Myriads of worms of many kinds lurk on or in the beach. Some of them glean food from sand or water. Others are fierce predators armed with sickle jaws.

Most seashore worms appear nothing like earthworms – the only worms that many of us know. Some wear hairy coats; some sprout tentacles; some are rainbow coloured; some are tiny; one may be as long as any snake on earth.

The four main kinds of worms found on the shore are flatworms, roundworms, ribbon worms, and bristle worms. Flatworms are flat, brown or whitish creatures no longer than a fingernail. They seem to flow along on rocks and seaweed.

Roundworms are tiny, smooth-bodied, pointed worms that lurk in mud, beneath stones, or inside seaweeds. Many kinds live as parasites on other animals.

Ribbon worms are slimy, black or reddish predators, found under stones or on seaweed. If you uncoiled a so-called bootlace worm and dangled one end from a rooftop, the other end might brush the ground.

But the worms you are most likely to see upon the beach are bristle worms, named from the bristles that jut from the segments or compartments that make up the creatures' bodies. We may conveniently divide seashore bristle worms into two kinds according to their way of life. Some freely move around by swimming, wriggling, or crawling. Others build a protective tube and never leave it.

Active Bristle Worms
Members of various families of active bristle worms live on many beaches. These

Some of the sea worms found among rocks, gravels, sand, and mud. Each kind has its own type of dwelling place. Apart from the flatworm (16) and the bootlace worm (4), which is a ribbon worm, all those shown are bristleworms, related to the garden earthworm. Active bristleworms pictured are the eunecid (1), a paddleworm (3), the scaleworm (6) and sea mouse (11), the clamworm (9), and the catworm (10). The rest are tube worms. These include the fanworms (2) and (13), and the peacock worm (14); the serpulid, (15): terebellid (5) and sand mason (8); the lugworm (12); and a *Pectinaria* (7).

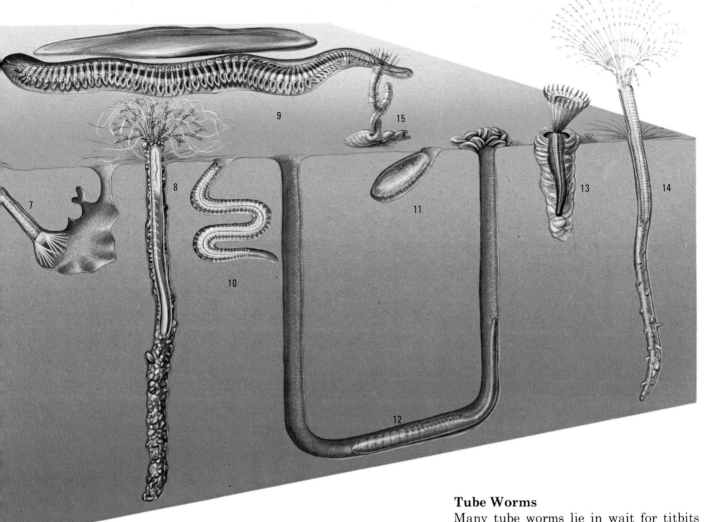

Below (enlarged): formidable jaws and teeth of the clamworm outthrust to seize a victim. At rest they lie inside the mouth.

families include scaleworms, paddleworms, ragworms, and catworms. A scaleworm's bristles have evolved as protective interlocking scales that guard its back. The so-called seamouse is a short, tubby scaleworm disguised by gleaming bristles and a mat of hairs that stop sand grains choking its breathing system.

Paddleworms have a pair of flattened 'paddles' projecting from each segment. These help the worms to swim around with the greatest ease.

Ragworms, on the other hand, lever their bodies along with their bristles as they prowl among the stones and seaweed, seeking prey. Ragworms seize victims, including other worms, with jaws that may be powerful enough to draw blood from a human finger.

Catworms resemble ragworms, but their bodies gleam like mother-of-pearl and their mouths are shaped for guzzling dead and decaying scraps rather than for grasping living prey.

Tube Worms

Many tube worms lie in wait for titbits that the sea brings to their doors. Such stay-at-home feeders include serpulid worms – tiny animals that hide in white, stony tubes glued to rocks and seaweeds. From the open end of its tube a serpulid worm thrusts feathery gills and snares tiny particles of food that waft past.

Peacock worms are larger and live in underground silt-and-mucus tubes as long as a man's foot. At high tide reddish tentacles peep from each tube top and fan out like a peacock's tail to capture food. Another fanworm, *Branchiomma*, uses stones and bits of shell to make a tube able to withstand the roughest waves.

The terebellid worms include yet another master builder – the sand mason, which hides inside a deep tunnel lined with mucus, sand, and stones. At high tide, terebellids send teams of threadlike tentacles writhing outwards over the sea floor in search of scraps of food.

But not all tube worms feed on or at the surface. The lugworm and the little *Pectinaria*, for example, live in burrows absorbing nourishment from the sand.

Armoured Animals

Crustaceans range from tiny grains of life called copepods to the giant spider crab with a two-metre claw span. Many kinds of crustacean haunt the shore.

In any rock pool you may meet at least one of the many kinds of armoured animals called crustaceans. Crustaceans belong to the arthropods – the great group of joint-legged animals that includes the insects and spiders. Crustaceans get their name from their crusty shells – hard yet more flexible than those of most molluscs.

Between them, the crustaceans grow whole toolkits of limbs variously designed for walking, swimming, and jumping. They breathe by means of gills and each has two pairs of feelers. But although they share this simple groundplan, crustaceans come in bewildering variety.

Crabs

Crabs, prawns, shrimps, and lobsters are decapods – animals with 10 walking legs sprouting from the thorax (the body section next to the head). Many crabs use their limbs to scuttle sideways and to dig down in sand. A crab's front legs bear powerful nippers that fend off enemies and grab dead or living creatures. The nippers then stuff these into the crab's mouth parts where several pairs of jaws break up the food. Crabs' limbs snap off in an emergency but soon regrow.

Most decapods have a flexible tail that they can tuck beneath the thorax. Many crabs always protect their soft underparts in this way. But hard-shelled crabs are soft and vulnerable when moulting – an event they must repeat as they grow.

Hermit crabs never grow a hard, protective shell. Instead, they guard themselves by living in the empty spiral homes of whelks or other one-shelled molluscs.

Lobsters, Prawns, and Shrimps

Like most crabs, lobsters are bottom dwellers and some kinds turn up in tidal pools from time to time. Lobsters somewhat resemble hermit crabs, but their long bodies are better armoured and end in a fan-like tail. Lobsters crawl about the sea floor as they scavenge for food. In emergency, a sudden forward flick of the tail sends a lobster darting backwards.

Crawfish, or spiny lobsters, closely resemble true lobsters, but lack their mighty pincers.

Much smaller than the lobsters and crawfish are their scavenging relatives the prawns and shrimps. Both swim with special hind-end appendages. But a prawn has two pairs of pincers to the shrimp's single pair, and a more rounded body. Also a shrimp lacks the prawn's rostrum – a forward projection of the shell between the eyes. Both creatures are only lightly armoured but swim too fast for many predators to catch them. Prawns roam the floors of rock pools. Shrimps prefer burrowing in sand.

Three views (much enlarged) of a young shore crab. Top: a recently hatched larva. Middle: the larva later, from above. Its abdomen (hind end) projects. Bottom: young crab, its hind end tucked in.

Isopods and Amphipods

The bodies of these little shore scavengers consist of a number of segments protected by overlapping 'armour plates'. The isopods' bodies are in most cases flattened from top to bottom. Their name means 'equal footed', and an isopod's seven pairs of legs are all much alike and designed for walking, not swimming. Common isopods include the sea slaters, closely resembling their landbound wood-lice relatives. Sea slaters themselves are land-lubbers and would eventually drown if kept under water. They live in cracks in rocks above high tide level, swarming out at night to gobble garbage washed up by the tides. Other isopods include some that can roll up in a ball if threatened, and the formidable wood-devouring gribble. Gribbles are just half a centimetre long, but thousands of these isopods burrowing through timbers have wrecked many a wooden harbour in the past.

Unlike the isopods, amphipods have bodies flattened from side to side. Their name comes from Greek words meaning 'both' and 'foot'. In fact most amphipods have three kinds of limbs: five pairs of walking legs, three pairs of swimmerets for swimming, and three pairs of uropods for jumping – hence their popular name 'sandhoppers'. Most amphipods live under seashore stones or in rotting seaweed, burrowing or wriggling on their sides.

Barnacles

Back in 1833 the British Army doctor John Vaughan Thompson astonished biologists by showing that barnacles were crustaceans, not molluscs as most people had believed. Most adult barnacles live fixed to rocks or other objects, their bodies hidden by hard, limy plates. But Thompson showed that barnacles start life as tiny creatures that swim freely in the sea. Eventually young barnacles settle on some hard substance, grow an armour-plated home around them, and turn their limbs into a net for trapping food.

Best-known barnacles are acorn barnacles, whose tiny, white, dome-like homes stud many rocks beside the sea. As the tide covers them, feathery projections move in and out between the shell plates, catching scraps of seaborne food and trapping oxygen. The stalked barnacles sometimes washed up on the beach live a similar life, but project from rubbery stalks usually attached to floating wood or bottles, or to underwater timbers. Another kind of barnacle is a parasite that fastens onto crabs and grows inside their bodies.

Crustaceans that may be seen at or near the sea's edge: prawn (1); stalked barnacles growing from a floating bottle (2); crawfish or spiny lobster (3); common lobster (4); spider crab (5); squat lobster (6); hermit crab in whelk shell, shared with a sea anemone (7); common shrimp (8); opossum shrimp (9); shore crab (10); mud crab (11); fiddler crab (12); acorn barnacles (13). The fiddler crab is an inhabitant of tropical shores.

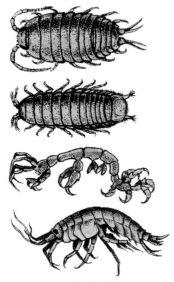

Above: beach-dwelling isopods and amphipods (magnified). Top: the sea slater (a crevice dweller) and gribble (a wood borer) are isopods. *Caprella linearis* (found among living seaweeds) and (bottom) the sandhopper, which lives in rotting seaweed, are amphipods.

Spiny Animals

What has no head, feet growing from its arms, and spines as weapons? The unlikely answer is a starfish – one of the strange animals known as echinoderms.

Starfish, sea urchins, and sea cucumbers belong to the echinoderm ('hedgehog skinned') group of animals. Some are spinier than others. But all have a body with at least five arms growing from a central disc, tube feet, and hard, limy plates under the skin. Echinoderms have no head, tail, or brain.

Starfish and Brittlestars

Equipped with five, flexible, leathery arms, many starfish remind us of five-pointed stars. Some, with extra arms, are sunflower-like. Others, with stubby arms, resemble five-sided plates.

On many a starfish the upper side bears tiny spines for defence. Each spine moves freely on a ball and socket joint. Special spines like birds' beaks can inflict a poisonous bite on enemies.

The underside of each arm bears rows of tiny holes through which the many tube feet peep. Each tiny foot grows from a muscular bottle fed with water from a pipe running through the centre of the arm. As muscles squeeze the bottle they drive water out and into the tube foot, forcing it to lengthen. Once water starts to flow back to the bottle the foot tip becomes a sucker. Starfish use their sucker feet to haul themselves along and to grip rocks so that storm waves cannot wrench their bodies loose.

Many starfish eat small crabs and other creatures whole. But to tackle a thick-shelled cockle a starfish twists the bivalve hinge upwards and climbs astride. Gripping tightly with its tube feet, the hunter prizes apart the two halves of the shell. Then the starfish forces part of its own stomach out through its mouth, located underneath the central disc. Turned inside out, the starfish stomach slips between the cockle's shell valves and begins to dissolve and digest the victim.

Unlike a starfish's disc, that of a brittlestar is easy to see and more obviously separate from the arms. A brittlestar's arms really do seem brittle – they readily snap off if handled. Brittlestars and starfish both regrow lost arms, and a lost starfish arm with a bit of disc attached grows into a brand new starfish.

The arms of a starfish (above) grip and walk with tube feet (above left). Water entering on top feeds into pipes and fills 'bottles' in each arm. Muscles squeeze water from each bottle into a foot, which lengthens. As water returns to the bottle the foot tip forms a sucker.

The sand dollar (above) is a close relative of the sea urchin. The brittlestar (below) has arms more separated than a starfish's.

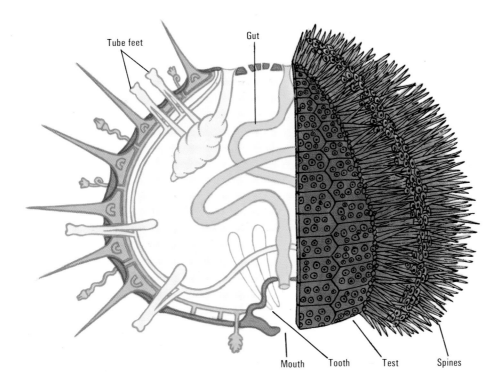

Tube feet

Gut

Mouth   Tooth   Test   Spines

This cutaway view of a sea urchin shows the hard test that forms a case around the body. Projecting from the test are spines that move on ball and socket joints. From tiny holes in the test poke tube feet operated by water-filled tubes and 'bottles' in the body. A mouth equipped with powerful teeth opens beneath the centre of the body. Food passes from the mouth through the gut, and body waste escapes by way of a hole at the top.

The sea urchin (above) is a prickly ball. Yet the sea urchin's body is built like that of a starfish. Both have spines, a mouth under the body, and five bands of tube feet that project through holes in the skin.

Sea Urchins and Sand Dollars

At first glance a sea urchin looks nothing like a starfish. It resembles a small, prickly pincushion bristling with long, narrow spines that jut in all directions from a hard, hollow shell known as a test. But if you examine a dead sea urchin with its spines removed you notice five bands bearing tiny holes that start at the sharp-toothed mouth beneath the test and end at the top. The holes are gaps for tube feet and the bands match the five arms of a starfish.

Different sea urchins have different feeding habits. Some browse on seaweed. Some use their five teeth to nip off barnacles or tube worms. Heart urchins lie buried in the sand, using long tube feet to grope around for seabed food. As in a starfish, body waste and eggs leave through holes at the middle of the body's upper side.

The sea urchin's nearest relative is the sand dollar – a thin, flat creature that lives half buried in the sand.

Sea Cucumbers

Many a sea cucumber is the shape and size of a gherkin, though some tropical kinds grow as long as a man's arm. At one end is the mouth surrounded by a bush of tube-feet tentacles for catching food. Five double rows of tube feet run lengthwise down the body.

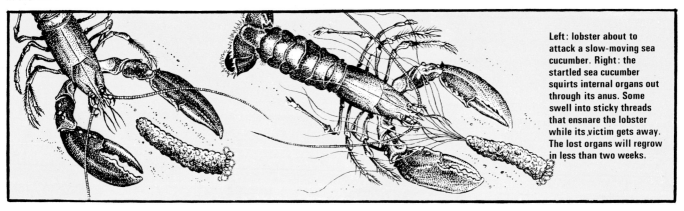

Left : lobster about to attack a slow-moving sea cucumber. Right : the startled sea cucumber squirts internal organs out through its anus. Some swell into sticky threads that ensnare the lobster while its victim gets away. The lost organs will regrow in less than two weeks.

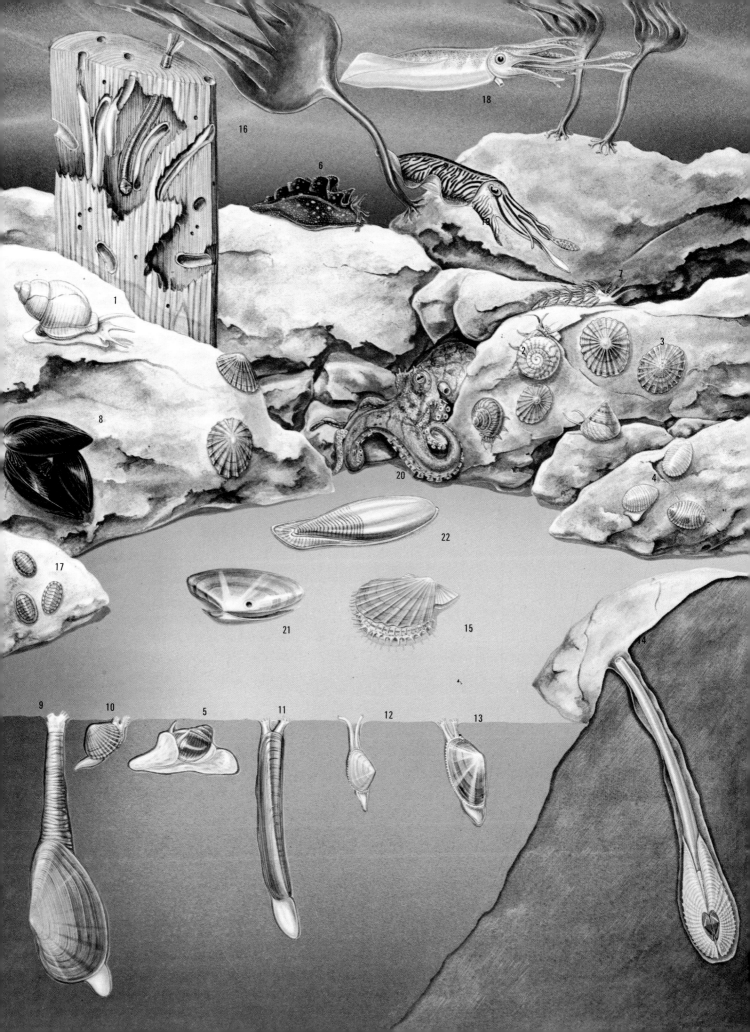

Animals with Shells

Dogwhelks, sea slugs, razor shells, and octopuses lead very different lives. Yet all belong to one group of soft-bodied, shell-bearing animals – the molluscs.

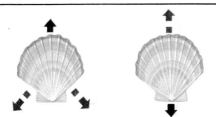

Unlike most bivalve molluscs, scallops have the remarkable ability of swimming. They do so by opening and shutting the shell valves rapidly like a bird snapping its beak. If a fleshy curtain covers the free end of the shell when the shell shuts, water squirts out backwards from the hinge end, forcing the scallop forwards. If the curtain is drawn aside when the shell shuts, water squirts out forwards from the free end and forces the scallop backwards through the water.

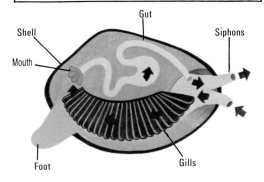

Cutaway view of a bivalve mollusc. Shell valves draw in water and drive out waste. This bivalve moves on a foot poked out between both valves.

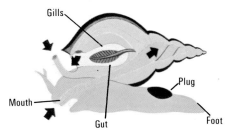

Cutaway view of a gastropod mollusc. A rasp-like ribbon scrapes off food. The creature can withdraw in its shell and block the doorway with a plug.

Molluscs in an underwater setting. Dogwhelk (1), topshell (2), limpet (3), cowries (4), and necklace shell (5) are all gastropods, protected by a single shell. (6) and (7) are sea slugs – gastropods that have lost their protective shells. Most of the rest live in shells with two hinged valves. These bivalve molluscs are mussels (8), soft-shelled clam (9), cockle (10), razor shell (11), tellin (12), wedge shell (13), piddock (14), scallop (15), and teredo 'worm' (16). Other molluscs are chitons (17) and three cephalopods: squid (18), cuttlefish (19), and octopus (20). On the sea bed are the pierced shell (21) of a mollusc killed by the necklace shell, and a cuttlebone (22).

For most of us the sea shells strewn about the beach are no more than pretty ornaments. For the animals that lived inside them they were life-preservers, protecting the creatures' bodies from battering by sand and sea and from their would-be eaters. Aptly enough, these tender-bodied animals are known as molluscs from a Latin word for 'soft'. All molluscs have a three-part body: a powerful foot for moving, body organs placed above the foot, and shell-producing tissue called the mantle.

Gastropods and Bivalves

The great group of gastropod ('stomach footed') molluscs includes shellfish owning a head with eyes and protected by a single shell. Beneath shells like Chinese coolies' hats, limpets crouch on rocks, and at high tide scrape off seaweed with a radula – a horny ribbon armed with tiny teeth. A sea snail such as a periwinkle, topshell or dogwhelk has a spiral shell and attaches its body to a pillar running through the middle. A startled sea snail pulls its foot into the shell, and blocks the opening with a leathery plug borne on the foot. But the meat-eating dogwhelks and necklace shells can drill or dissolve holes through mollusc shells.

Sea slugs are gastropods that have practically lost their shells. If threatened, the sea slug called a sea hare squirts a purple-ink smokescreen that aids escape. Other sea slugs rely on camouflage.

Bivalves have a shell of two hinged halves or valves. They lack a head, but hardly need it. Instead of roaming after food, a bivalve simply sieves food particles from water drawn in through a tube known as a siphon. It employs another siphon to squirt used water out. Some bivalves take food from the water above. Others use siphons shaped like tiny elephants' trunks to dredge the sea floor.

Mussels can latch onto rocks with a web of threads, but many bivalves burrow in the sand or mud. The razor shell, a master burrower in sand, plunges downwards almost faster than a man can dig. The misnamed teredo 'worm' drives long tunnels into wood, while piddocks bore deep dens in soft rocks such as chalk and limestone.

Chitons and Cephalopods

Chitons or coat-of-mail shells form a third great group of molluscs. These flattened, oval animals no longer than a finger joint cling like limpets to the rocks, and browse by means of radulas. Eight overlapping plates protect each chiton's body. If the creature is dislodged it curls up like a woodlouse.

You often see a cuttlebone washed up on the shore. This is the large internal shell of the cuttlefish. But only the lowest tides reveal a living cuttlefish or its relatives the squid and octopus. In all these cephalopod ('head-footed') molluscs the foot is big and divided into arms that help the creatures seize their prey. To move one way cephalopods simply use a siphon to squirt water in the opposite direction. They are truly jet propelled.

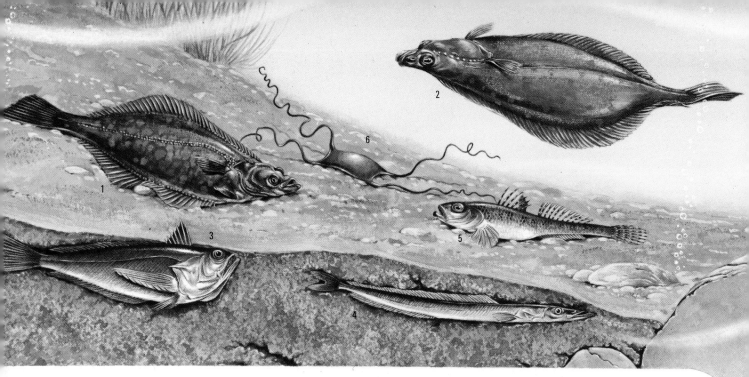

Above: fishes found off some sandy shores. Plaice (1) and (2) are flatfishes. Lesser weever (3) and lesser sand eel (4) are burrowers. The sand goby's body (5) is superbly camouflaged. A skate or its egg case (6) may appear inshore. Below: stages in a flatfish's growth. It starts like a normal fish, but its skull warps until both eyes are on one side.

Grunions washed up at high tide lay eggs on Californian beaches. The female digs into the sand to lay the eggs. Waves then sweep the fishes out to sea again.

Fishes of the Shore

Ribbon thin and pancake flat are two of the unusual shapes that help inshore fishes to dodge storms or enemies. Each species has its own secrets of survival.

At some of the highest tides on spring and summer nights an unbelievable scene takes place on certain Californian beaches. As a wave sucks back down the beach it leaves behind a wriggling mass of slim, silvery fishes each about the length of a man's hand. These animals are grunions. Each stranded female proceeds to lay up to 3,000 eggs in the sand. Males fertilize the eggs. Then both sexes catch the next high wave back out to sea. A fortnight later another extra-high tide sweeps in and bares the eggs, from which young grunions burst like popcorn.

Few other seashore fishes dare to run such risks of drying up or being caught by land animals. Indeed most shore fishes are cleverly designed to stay below the tossing waves and out of sight.

Fishes of Rocky Shores
Many of these creatures have long, narrow bodies flattened from side to side – ideal for squeezing between rocks. Roll over a boulder low down on the beach at an extremely low tide and you may expose a snake-like conger eel as long as a man's arm. At the other end of the size scale is the little finger-length blenny called a butterfish which crouches under stones.

The small, blunt-headed gobies and elbow-length, hump-backed lumpsuckers possess underbody suckers. These help them cling to the seabed when storms send waves crashing ashore.

Fishes of rocky shores feed on a variety of diets. Wrasses have powerful teeth that crunch up shellfish whole. The blennies' wide teeth can rasp off rock-hugging barnacles and bivalves. Sea scor-

pions' gaping mouths gulp in shrimps. The snakelike pipe fishes suck up tiny plankton animals. Spines help to protect sea scorpions and sticklebacks from fishes that would feed upon them.

Many fishes of rocky coasts guard their eggs from the force of the waves. The male 15-spined stickleback, for instance, builds a seaweed nest. The butterfish smears its eggs inside a clam shell.

Fishes of Sand and Mud

Life on soft, sandy shores has helped to produce fishes differently designed from those that live among rocks. Here live such flatfishes as the flounder, plaice, and dab – pancake-flat animals fringed with ribbon-like fins. Lying dark side up on a sandy sea floor, a plaice becomes invisible. The little sand goby's sandy body is also splendidly camouflaged. But weevers and sand eels hide by burying themselves, the slender sand eels using their long lower jaws as living shovels. Unlike the sand eels, weevers have powerful defensive weapons: poisonous spines jutting from their backs.

All these fishes are carnivorous. For instance, flatfishes crunch up shellfish, sea worms, and crustaceans. Sand eels snap up their own and other fishes' young. The lesser weever grabs shrimps.

No fishes are better designed for life on muddy shores than the mudskippers of tropical mangrove swamps. These small, pop-eyed creatures can haul out on wet mud, breathe by gulping air and water, and jerk along by using fins as crutches. Some kinds chew seaweed, others browse on algae in the mud. But most hunt sandhoppers and tiny crabs.

Above: fishes found off some rocky shores. The corkwing wrasse (7) swims among the seaweeds. The sea scorpion (8), butterfish (9), and conger eel (10) cram their slim bodies into rock crannies. An underbelly sucker anchors the lumpsucker (11). The 15-spined stickleback (12) hides under seaweed and stones. Snake pipefishes (13) cling by their tails.

Mudskipper on a Seychelles island shore. These pop-eyed amphibious fishes teem in mangrove swamps.

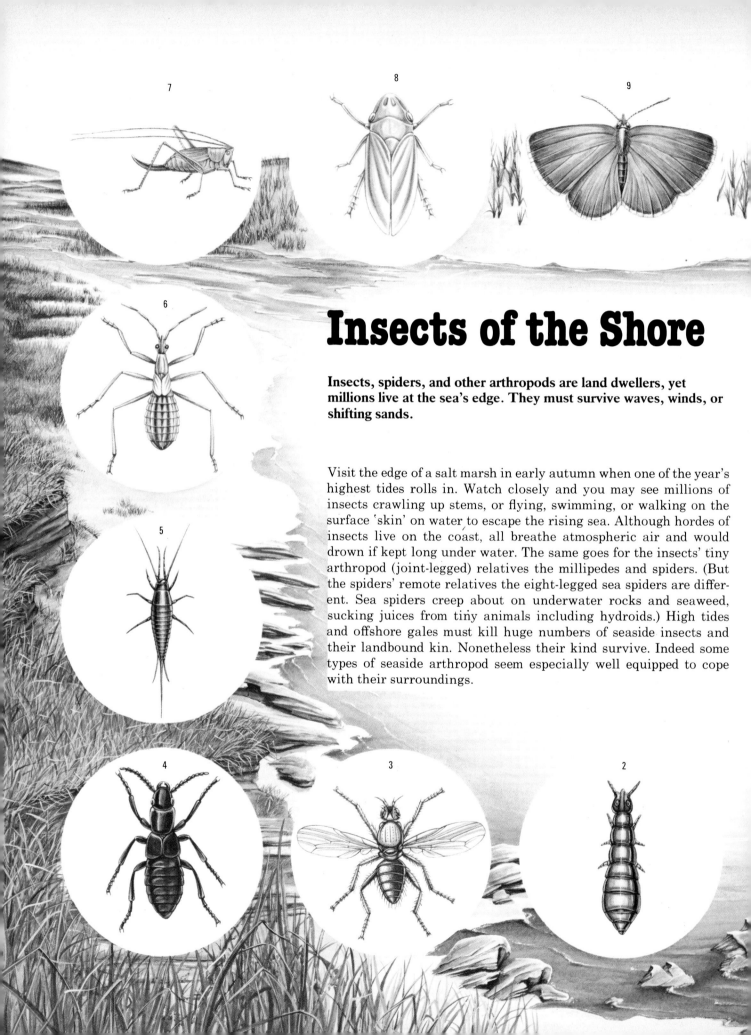

Insects of the Shore

Insects, spiders, and other arthropods are land dwellers, yet millions live at the sea's edge. They must survive waves, winds, or shifting sands.

Visit the edge of a salt marsh in early autumn when one of the year's highest tides rolls in. Watch closely and you may see millions of insects crawling up stems, or flying, swimming, or walking on the surface 'skin' on water to escape the rising sea. Although hordes of insects live on the coast, all breathe atmospheric air and would drown if kept long under water. The same goes for the insects' tiny arthropod (joint-legged) relatives the millipedes and spiders. (But the spiders' remote relatives the eight-legged sea spiders are different. Sea spiders creep about on underwater rocks and seaweed, sucking juices from tiny animals including hydroids.) High tides and offshore gales must kill huge numbers of seaside insects and their landbound kin. Nonetheless their kind survive. Indeed some types of seaside arthropod seem especially well equipped to cope with their surroundings.

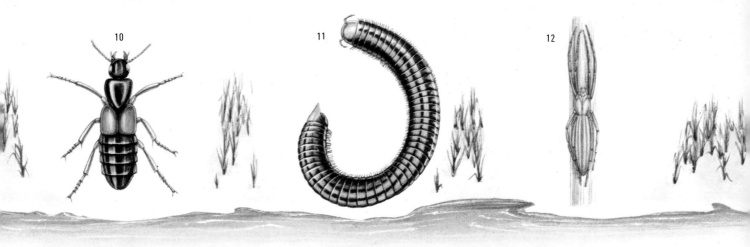

Twelve insects and other arthropods (enlarged) that live on various types of shore. This sea spider (1), an underwater relative of land spiders, lives low down on rocky shores. Next come four insects of rocky shores: a springtail (2); a seaweed fly (3), also found on sandy shores; a beetle (4); and a bristletail (5). Insects inhabiting salt marsh include this damsel bug (6); bush cricket (7); and bug (8). The sandy shore or the dunes provide homes for the butterfly (9) and rove beetle (10), the snake millipede (11), and this spider (12).

Insect life in fresh-water ponds and streams is extremely abundant. It is surprising, therefore, that so few insects have taken to life in the ocean. In fact, there is only one known insect that goes through all its stages in the sea – a tropical midge *Clunio marinus*. The female has no wings or front legs. The male has short wings that are almost useless for flight.

The pond skater, an insect that can walk on the water's surface layer, also lives on the surface of the ocean, sometimes hundreds of miles out to sea.

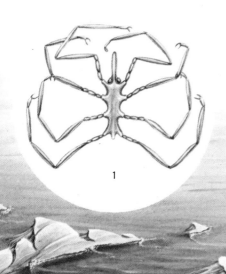

1

On Rocky Shores

Two insects found on rocky shores are a springtail and a bristletail. Springtails take their name from a kind of spring beneath their bodies. A springtail that suddenly releases its spring makes a mighty jump. Bristletails much resemble their relatives the silverfish that live in many kitchens. Springtails and bristletails hide in crannies at high tide, later creeping out to scavenge plant or animal remains. Lacking wings, these tiny insects are unlikely to be blown away to sea. And if waves swamp the springtail, its hairy body traps enough air to last it several days.

The seaweed flies are also well designed for seashore life. These insects lay their eggs in the seaweed cast high up on the shore. The warm slime of the rotting weed provides enough food and heat to keep their maggots growing – even in the depths of winter. The adult insects tend to fly too low, fast, and briefly to be blown offshore. But should winds tumble them onto the sea, their greasy, waterproof bodies buoy them up and they can soon take off.

Shore beetles and centipedes that lurk under stones or in rock crevices also make a living on the rocky shore.

On Sands and Salt Marsh

Many arthropods live on or near sandy shores. For instance, wingless rove beetles burrow by the thousands in the upper sands of northern European beaches. Dwellers in the dunes behind the beach include millipedes and spiders able to survive in dry sand. One so-called crab spider stands with four legs forward and four backward, blending invisibly with the blade of marram grass on which it lurks in wait for prey. Another dune spider lays eggs in a bowl scooped from the sand, and lines and roofs the bowl with threads that help to stop the eggs from drying up. Sand grains sticking to the threads help to hide the eggs from predators. Beetles, flies, wasps, bees, and ants all abound in many seashore dunes.

Salt marshes can also prove rich hunting grounds for insect life. Someone once counted 250 kinds of insect in the salt marshes of North Carolina in the eastern USA. Here, food and shelter affect the kinds of insect found more than the tides do. Thus the slim, tough stems of a rush attract the same types of insects that you find on similar plants that grow inland. A quiet salt marsh hides life and death struggles between insect hunters and hunted. In one English salt marsh biologists found that plant-eating bugs often fell prey to bush crickets, themselves sought out by ferocious flies.

Reptiles on the Beach

Reptiles were the first backboned animals designed for life on dry land. Yet some gave rise to seagoing beasts – the marine turtles and marine lizards.

Heaving herself along on flippers, a huge marine turtle hauls ashore on a sandy Malayan beach to lay eggs in the secrecy of night. Her ridged back betrays this as a leatherback, the world's largest living turtle species.

Marine turtles come in various shapes and sizes. Largest are the leatherbacks, some longer than a man, weighing more than half a tonne, and reinforced by seven struts along the back and five struts underneath the body. Leatherbacks eat squid and fishes. Next largest is the green turtle, a smooth-shelled herbivore well over one metre long. Green turtles have been much hunted as a source of turtle soup. Loggerheads may reach one metre. They like to hunt crustaceans, echino-derms, and molluscs in quiet bays. The ridley and the hawksbill are the two smallest species attaining one metre or less. Ridleys chiefly eat crustaceans. Hawksbills can tackle sting-ing jellyfish. Tortoiseshell comes from the dark, mottled, horny plates on the hawksbills' backs. To get it, hunters sometimes capture hawksbills with a lassooed shark sucker — a fish that sticks onto the turtle, which can then be hauled up into a waiting boat.

Turtles on the Sands

A large shape looms up at night in the waves breaking on a tropical ocean beach. For a while the object lies in the breakers. Then the great beast slowly heaves itself up onto the sand. A green turtle is coming ashore to lay her eggs.

She seems ill designed for the task. Her vast, flat forelimbs make excellent oars for rowing through water, and her short, broad hindlimbs are superb rudders. But this huge sea-going reptile weighs up to a third of a tonne. Out of water her breast-stroke flipper movements can hump her body along at only a metre or two a minute. Snorting groans mark her slow, flopping path up the beach. She often stops to rest, and the effort of moving on land seems to bring tears to her eyes. But she is really shedding the surplus salt that collects in her body during her life spent out at sea.

After half an hour or more, the turtle has reached the dry, loose surface sand above spring-tide level. Here she begins to dig with her hind flippers. An hour later she has gouged a flask-shaped pit up to a metre deep in the sand. Then she starts laying. Soon, as many as 200 white eggs as big as billiard balls lie in the nest hole, and the mother's next task is to hide them from predators by shovelling sand over the eggs with her flippers. At last she lumbers back to the sea, her limbs leaving tell-tale 'tank tracks' in the sand.

Six more times (with fortnightly breaks) the turtle may haul ashore to lay eggs. Finally she swims off to browse on the so-called turtle grass that grows in sub-marine meadows, perhaps hundreds of miles away.

Ridley turtle

Loggerhead turtle

Hawksbill turtle

Green turtle

Leatherback turtle

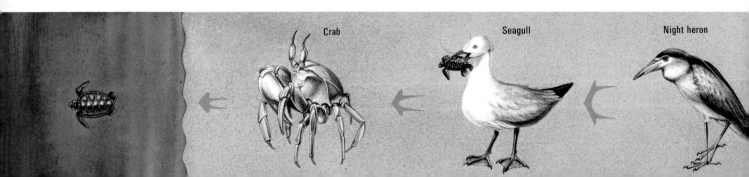

Crab   Seagull   Night heron

Not prehistoric monsters but living lizards basking on a Galápagos Islands shore. As with all reptiles, the marine iguanas' body temperature and thus their liveliness depends upon the warmth of their surroundings.

For eight hatchling turtles (below right) the road to the sea is an obstacle race where the obstacles are killers. Turtles that escape peccaries may have to get by frigate birds, coyotes, night-herons, seagulls, and crabs. In our illustration, one in eight of the turtles that set out gets through to the sea. In reality the survival rate is far lower.

Death Race to the Sea

Warmed by the sun, the turtle's eggs start to develop, perhaps with thousands more laid nearby at the same time by hundreds of other green turtles.

Many eggs will never hatch. Some prove infertile. Others get scooped up and eaten by jaguars, tigers, raccoons, wild dogs, big monitor lizards or men.

But after roughly two months of development, fertile eggs crack open. Hatchlings no bigger than the palm of a man's hand break from their shells and squirm to the beach surface. Now a turtle army starts to race for the sea. Very few of its members will get there. As if by magic, hordes of predators appear and attack, and the little beasts are plucked up by frigate birds, snatched by crabs, or grabbed by gulls, night herons, dogs, coyotes or opossums. Fewer than one in 100 hatchlings may reach the relative safety of the waves.

The plight of the hatchling green turtles is repeated for their marine relatives, the hawksbill, ridley and loggerhead, and the huge leatherback turtle. Yet, somehow, enough hatchlings survive to assure the species' survival.

Lizards on the Rocks

A gecko on Malpelo Island off Colombia catches crabs, and several other kinds of lizard live on sea shores. But the marine iguanas of the Galápagos Islands are unique. The big, black lizards bask and breed on the rocky shores of these volcanic outcrops in the eastern Pacific Ocean. But marine iguanas actually feed in the sea. They plunge off rocks, swim by waving their long tails (flattened from side to side) and walk on the sea floor. There they browse upon sargassum weed that thrives on surf-battered rocks. The lizards must often cling grimly to the rocks to stop waves from sweeping them away.

Coyote   Frigate bird   White-lipped peccary

Birds on the Shore

For gulls, terns, wading birds and others, beaches offer food-rich snack bars. For some, too, sea cliffs provide nurseries safe from landbound predators.

On many a shore, flocks of birds take wing as you approach. Others wheel around the cliffs above your head. Birds may also fly, swim, and dive above, on, and in the shallow waters, for many kinds find food or nesting sites, near the sea's edge.

Birds on Cliffs and Rocks

Some birds have their homes on sea cliffs. Gulls, guillemots, razorbills, gannets, fulmars, cormorants, and their seabird kin nest on narrow cliffside ledges. These ledges not only offer safety from rats and foxes. They are vantage points from which the birds can often spy passing shoals of fish and plummet down upon them like feathered dive bombers. Long, tapering gliders' wings help gulls and other seabirds to ride the winds that blow up cliffs, and to circle effortlessly out to sea in search of dead and living fishes.

Gulls also seek titbits washed up on the beach. But other birds are more especially designed for living here. Among these are the oystercatchers – smart, black-and-white wading birds with long legs and red bills that are chisel tipped and flattened at the sides. Oystercatchers' bills can hammer open bivalves or slip between the opened valves of an underwater mussel and cut the fleshy fibres with which the mussel shuts it valves. Turnstones are waders that really do turn stones as they search for insects, molluscs, and crustaceans. Stubbily built purple sandpipers pick little crabs and winkles from rock crevices, and snatch gobies from rock pools. Among the stranded seaweed, rock pipits dodge about for flies and sandhoppers, much as wagtails dart about near streams and rivers.

Some seabirds and shorebirds of northern coasts. Among those that perch or nest on cliffs are herring gulls (1), guillemot (2), fulmar (3), puffin (4), gannet (5), and razorbill (6). Manx shearwaters (7) nest in holes on clifftop banks. A cormorant (8) rests on the rocky beach, where purple sandpipers (9), oystercatchers (10), turnstones (11) and rock pipits (12) hunt for food. Out to sea are summer visitors – the common terns (13) – and a winter visitor – the goldeneye duck (14). Sanderlings (15) and ringed plover (16) range along a sandy beach. The muddy shore is a hunting ground for dunlin (17), redshank (18), and curlews (19). The spoonbill (20), flamingo (21), avocet (22) and blackwinged stilt (23) haunt lagoons inshore. Flamingos seldom range very far north.

Birds of Sands and Mud

Seashore bird life is often at its most abundant on low, sandy and muddy shores. This is not surprising, for no farm soil is so rich in small food animals as a beach of muddy sand.

At the sea's very edge on a sandy beach small, nimble sanderlings dart after the receding waves to snatch sandhoppers. Higher up the beach ringed plovers run, pause, and pluck up lugworms betrayed by their vibrations in the sand. Dunlin, knots and other waders gorge on maggots in the rotting seaweed.

On muddy shores, long-legged, long-billed redshanks probe and pry. Many birds of the mudflats have bills purpose made for special ways of feeding. Curlews thrust their long, downcurved bills deep down. Avocets trap food particles by sweeping their upcurved bills sideways through water. Spoonbills sweep their spoon-shaped bills in semicircles. Flamingos sieve muddy water through bent, bristle-fringed beaks to snare tiny insect larvae, crustaceans and molluscs.

Behind some muddy shores lies salt marsh – a valuable grazing ground for geese.

Birds on the Sea

The sea itself is yet another breadbasket. Terns gracefully wing above the surface and dive to snatch up sand eels. Sea ducks squat low in the water, then plunge for such seabed snacks as crabs, shrimps, worms, and molluscs. In some warm countries, squadrons of pelicans zoom down to share the fishes with gulls, cormorants and other seabirds.

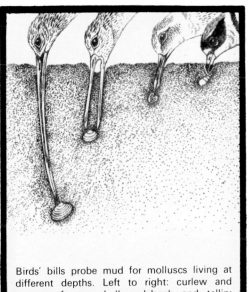

Birds' bills probe mud for molluscs living at different depths. Left to right: curlew and peppery furrow shell; redshank and tellin; sanderling and cockle; ringed plover and hydrobia snail. Beak length determines diet.

Mammals

Some sea mammals waddle weakly on land. But many haul ashore to sunbathe, moult, or breed.

In summer from an island hilltop in the chilly Bering Sea you may glimpse about 100,000 wild mammals – more than from any other vantage point on earth. The island is St. Paul. The mammals are northern fur seals and their pups.

Fur seals belong to the eared seals, one of the three types of seal. The other two are the true seals and the walrus. All these sea mammals are descended from ancestors that lived on land. But with limbs evolved as flippers, seals are designed for life in water. Most come ashore only to bask, moult, or breed. Some never touch land but pup on ice in the cold waters of the world's far north and south.

Seals Ashore

When seals haul ashore, some prove clumsier than others. True seals cannot turn their trailing hindlimbs forward, and resemble giant maggots as they work their short, weak forelimbs to heave themselves along. Eared seals (these are the fur seals and sealions) can rotate their hindlimbs forward and raise their bodies off the surface. They can even gallop and leap over rocks, relying on strong front flippers, soft springy ribs, and blubber (thick body fat) to break a fall. Walruses can also bring their hindlimbs forward and lollop along the beach.

Thick blubber or dense hair traps body heat and prevents beached seals from chilling in cold air. On hot days, however, their insulated bodies may overheat. Some seals cool off by waving their flippers. Others plunge into the sea. Overheated walruses blush rosy red as vessels in their skin fill with blood and act as radiators.

Unless disturbed, moulting and basking

Life in a crowded breeding colony of northern fur seals on one of the Pribilof Islands of the Bering Sea. This family scene shows a big bull beachmaster with his many, much smaller, wives, and their pups.

seals just like to lie around. Possibly this helps the moulting process, which sometimes must be painful. At any rate strips of skin peel off with clumps of hair from moulting elephant seals. These vast beasts (males can exceed three tonnes) rest in their hundreds in muddy pools behind the beach. Perhaps mud soothes their irritated hides.

Seal Nurseries

Breeding seals are often more lively on the shore than moulting seals, especially the rather agile northern fur seals. The adult bulls land in May or June and start to fight for territory. Each successful bull or 'beachmaster' defends his strip of beach throughout the breeding season. Meanwhile, for two months or more, he fasts, nourished only by the hump of fat that bulges from the back of his neck.

Every beachmaster gathers a harem of some 40 wives from among the cows that now swim in. Before they mate again, most adult cows give birth to a single black pup, and soon the beach is dark with fur-seal families.

Not all the fur-seal pups live long. Many die of hookworm or (if they lose their mothers) of starvation, or are trampled by their fighting fathers. This last risk is also great among the bulky elephant seals, one of only two kinds of true seal to form and fight for harems.

But most fur-seal pups do survive, and they develop quickly. By 10 days old they play with other pups. Within a month they paddle in seashore pools. At three months they swim freely. In November the pups are weaned and move off to sea. By December only a few bachelor fur seals remain on the once-teeming beach.

The elephant seal (1) and grey seal (2) belong to the true seals. The elephant seal, the world's largest seal, is named for its great bulk and for the male's long, trunk-like nose. Its homes include islands off California. The smaller grey seal lives off coasts from North America east to the Baltic Sea. The Californian sealion (3) is one of the eared seals. The walrus (4) lives only in cold waters.

Below: a sea otter floating on its back. Lying comfortably like this, the animal will bash a sea shell against a stone laid on its chest until the shell is broken. Then the otter eats the shell's contents.

Sea otters — once nearly wiped out for their fur by hunters — live around certain coasts of the North Pacific Ocean. Like the seals, sea otters are land mammals that have taken to the sea, and indeed their hind limbs have evolved as paddle feet somewhat resembling a sealion's flippers. Sea otters swim with their paddle feet and dive to the sea bed for such snacks as sea urchins and shellfish. To open a big shellfish, many a sea otter floats on its back with a large stone resting on its chest. The stone then serves as an anvil against which the otter bangs the shell until it breaks. Scientists say this is one of the few examples of an animal deliberately choosing and using an object as a kind of tool.

The sea otters of California never set foot on a beach, but feed, breed, and groom themselves among floating seaweed off the shore. But farther north, on the Aleutian Islands, sea otters climb ashore at night to sleep, and by day if storms make diving difficult. Off northeast Asia, sea otters regularly rest by day on reefs of the Russian-owned Commander Islands. These otters also give birth to their cubs or 'kits' on land.

Man and the Shore

Most of us value the shore as a playground or a source of food. But man's misuse threatens beaches as we know them.

Man has changed many shorelines by building walls to keep the sea at bay.

Above: wind-blown waves that strike a sandy shore obliquely push sand along the shore as they advance, and pull it back to sea as they retreat. This movement shifts sands along the coast. Below: groynes that jut into the sea help to stop the coastwise drift of sand and thus tend to build the beach outwards.

Using the Shore

Man is a land animal, but the sea shore has always beckoned him. People first came to the coast for food and found it everywhere. Hardy islanders learnt to climb sea cliffs for seabirds and their eggs. Wildfowlers hunted on the marshes. Food-gatherers prized winkles and limpets from the rocks, and scooped shrimps, mussels, oysters, soft-shelled clams, and turtles' eggs from mud or sand. Hunters came clubbing seals for meat and fur. Fishermen brought lines, nets, and traps. Some food gatherers became shellfish farmers, cultivating bivalves on the sea bed. This still proves well worth the trouble, for in one year a given patch of mussel bed may yield 50 times more meat than the same area of best pasture grazed by cattle. Curiously, tastes in sea foods differ. The British seldom eat soft-shelled clams, an American delicacy. Similarly some Europeans prize sea urchins, squid, and sea squirts, yet others will not touch them.

Earlier we saw that certain peoples eat seaweed. Seaweeds also serve as fertilizer. Brown seaweeds supply fodder for sheep in the Orkney Islands north of Scotland. Two centuries ago people burnt brown seaweed to extract soda and potash. Most of the soda used for making glass once came from seaweed. Last century, men also learnt to extract the medically valuable substance iodine from seaweed. Today, some red seaweeds have another medical use; as the source of agar, a jelly on which bacteria will grow in the laboratory.

Besides exploiting seashore plants and animals, man often employs the very substances of which the shore is made. Quarrymen long ago began hacking limestone from sea cliffs in southern England. In many lands builders have removed huge loads of sand from shores and dunes for making concrete. Sands from Australia and India are now valued for the minerals they hold. Then, too, many a cove, bay, and estuary shore has formed the building site for a fishing village, port, or holiday resort.

Changing the Shore

Where man settles by the sea he often alters the shore. If storm waves threaten seaside roads or houses, engineers line the shore with massive walls to keep the sea at bay. Engineers also build walls jutting out toward the sea – groynes that create beaches by trapping drifting sands and shingle. By raising walls between islands and pumping out the trapped seawater, the Dutch have even pushed shorelines far out to sea.

Man is also drastically altering life on the shore. In South-East Asia American troops poisoned huge tracts of coastal mangroves to rob enemies of hiding places. Sealions and shore birds died off California when rivers washed farm pesticides into the sea. An oil spill once clogged and killed more than 1,000 eider ducks in Scotland's Tay estuary; elsewhere oil spills, have annihilated millions of seashore plants and animals. In Japan, coast-dwelling people died after eating shellfish poisoned by carelessly discharged factory waste. In some estuaries, city sewage has suffocated most forms of life. As man's factories and cities grow, their wastes increase, multiplying the risks to seashore life. Yet the controlled release of city waste can prevent disasters.

A century ago our ancestors discovered that no place was more entrancing for a holiday than a healthy seashore, clothed with living plants and animals. Today, only by taking the greatest care shall we keep alive the magic of the shore.

This ship sprays special liquid on the sea to disperse an oil slick. Oil spilt from tankers sometimes floats ashore, clogging beaches and killing seashore life. Thus human accident or carelessness can devastate vast stretches of coast.

Millions of families enjoy holidays on beaches such as this. Swimming, sunbathing, and the wildlife of the shore offer never-ending fascination. But pollution will ruin coasts unless man keeps them free from the wastes his way of life creates.

Index

Acknowledgments

Photographs: Page 5 Heather Angel; 6 Heather Angel; 7 Heather Angel; 8 ZEFA; 9 P. Morris; 12 ZEFA; 14 P. Morris; 16 P. Morris; 17 Heather Angel; 18 Heather Angel; 19 Heather Angel; 20 ZEFA; 22 Heather Angel; 23 Biofotos (top), Heather Angel (centre & bottom); 28 Heather Angel; 29 P. Morris; 32 Bruce Coleman Ltd.; 33 Heather Angel; 36 P. Morris; 37 Heather Angel; 40 ZEFA; 41 P. Morris; 42 ZEFA (top), NHPA (centre); 43 Shell Photo Service (top), ZEFA (bottom).